Practise ratios like a pro with CGP!

This fantastic CGP book is the best way to help pupils master KS2 Ratio and Proportion skills for the Maths SATs.

It's packed with quick-fire 10-Minute Tests that become more challenging as pupils work through — by the end they'll feel really confident with these tricky topics.

We've even included detailed answers for every question — plus a useful chart to check progress too!

What CGP is all about

Our sole aim here at CGP is to produce the highest quality books — carefully written, immaculately presented and dangerously close to being funny.

Then we work our socks off to get them out to you — at the cheapest possible prices.

Published by CGP

Editors: Adam Bartlett, Tom Miles and David Ryan

With thanks to Rachel Murray for the reviewing.
With thanks to Michael Bushell for the proofreading.

ISBN: 978 1 78908 453 5

Clipart from Corel®
Printed by Elanders Ltd, Newcastle upon Tyne.

Based on the classic CGP style created by Richard Parsons.

Contents

How to Use this Book

- This book contains <u>12 tests</u>, all geared towards improving your ratio and proportion skills.

- Each test is out of <u>10 marks</u> and should take about <u>10 minutes</u> to complete.

- Each test starts with some <u>warm-up questions</u> to get you going and ends with a <u>problem solving question</u>.

- The tests <u>increase in difficulty</u> as you go through the book.

- <u>Answers</u> and a <u>Progress Chart</u> can be found at the <u>back</u> of the book.

Warm up

1. What is:

   a) 10% of 30? ......3......   b) 50% of 8? ......4......

   c) 50% of 20? ......10......   d) 10% of 50? ......5......

   _____
   2 marks

2. a) How many times larger is 21 than 7? ......3......

   b) How many times larger is 30 than 2? ......15......

   _____
   2 marks

---

3. Look at these number cards.

   | ~~10~~ | ~~120~~ | 4 | 50 | ~~40~~ | 65 |

   Use the number cards to complete these percentage machines.

   One has been done for you.

   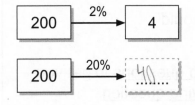

   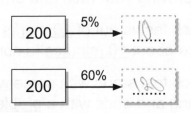

   _____
   2 marks

4. The distance between London and Vancouver is 7000 km.
   The distance between London and Paris is 350 km.

   How many times further is London from Vancouver than from Paris?

   ......20......

   _____
   1 mark

---

5. In summer, the level of water in a lake decreases by 10% compared to the level in winter.

In winter, the level of the water was 240 cm.

What is the level of the water in summer?

.............216.... cm

6. Albert is making a salmon dish for 2 people.
His recipe below shows the ingredients for 6 people.

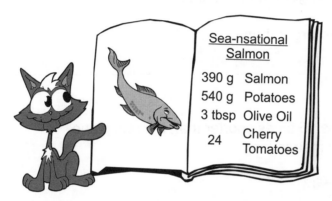

Sea-nsational
Salmon

390 g   Salmon
540 g   Potatoes
3 tbsp Olive Oil
24   Cherry
        Tomatoes

How many cherry tomatoes will he need?

.................8....... cherry tomatoes

How much salmon will he need?

.................130..... g

END OF TEST

/ 10

⏱10

Warm up

1. What is:

    a) 25% of 40? .... b) 10% of 70? ....

    c) 50% of 6? .... d) 20% of 50? ....

    _____
    2 marks

2. Fill in the gap to complete these statements.

    a) 18 is three times larger than ....

    b) 28 is seven times larger than ....

    _____
    2 marks

3. A model of a plane is <u>15 times shorter</u> than the real plane.
    The real plane is 60 metres long.

    How long is the model?

    .... m
    _____
    1 mark

4. Megan has £600. She spends 30% of her money on a new camera.

    How much does Megan spend on her new camera?

    £ ....
    _____
    1 mark

4

5. A shop sells greeting cards in two different boxes.
Box A contains 5 cards and costs £10.
Box B contains 10 cards and costs £18.

Which box is better value?

You must show all of your working.

Box ....

2 marks

6. A ranger works at a deer park. She says,

"Red deer have bodies that
are twice as long as their antlers."

115 cm

80 cm

The diagram on the right shows the
lengths of the antlers of two red deer.

Work out the difference in
the lengths of their bodies.

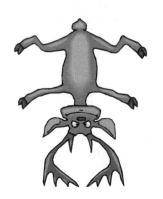

.... cm

2 marks

END OF TEST

/ 10

Warm up

1. What is:

   a) 20% × 15?

   b) 25% × 12?

   ....

   ....

   c) 80% × 20?

   d) 75% × 16?

   ....

   ....

   _____
   4 marks

2. Rex can dig 5 holes in 2 minutes

   How long will it take him to dig 35 holes?

   .... minutes

   _____
   1 mark

3. Stonehenge is a stone monument in England.
   The diagram on the right shows part of Stonehenge.

   Priya makes a model of the stones in the diagram.
   Her model is 18 cm high.

   How **wide** is her model?

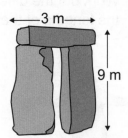

   .... cm

   _____
   1 mark

4. A 1.5 litre bottle of lemonade costs £1.15.
A 250 ml bottle of the same lemonade costs £0.20.

Hannah buys six 250 ml bottles and Jasper buys a 1.5 litre bottle.

How much more does Hannah pay than Jasper?

£ ....
_____
2 marks

5. Adam is making pastry. He needs 450 g of flour and 150 ml of water to make a small batch. A large batch uses 750 g of flour.

How much water will he need for the large batch?

.... ml
_____
2 marks

END OF TEST

/ 10

Warm up

1. What is:

   a) $\frac{1}{2}$ of 14? ....   b) $\frac{1}{6}$ of 18? ....

   _____
   1 mark

2. Fill in these boxes:

   a) 25% of 4000 = [   ]   b) 20% of 5000 = [   ]

   c) 50% of 10 000 = [   ]   d) 40% of 200 = [   ]

   _____
   2 marks

3. Sharla is planning a dance routine.
   It is split into 12 equal sections.
   Three sections take 45 seconds in total.

   How long does the whole dance take?

   .... seconds
   _____
   1 mark

4. Ki makes a cup of tea that is 90 °C.
   Her tea cools down by 4 °C every minute.
   Ki can drink her tea once it has cooled down to 54 °C.

   How long will Ki have to wait until she can drink her tea?

   .... minutes
   _____
   2 marks

5. A unicycle costs £50 and a tricycle costs £350.

    How many times more does a tricycle cost than a unicycle?

    ....   _____
                             1 mark

6. Tom has adopted a sausage dog.

    He is deciding which kennel to buy — A or B, shown below.
    The heights of the two kennels are in the ratio 2 : 3.

    Write the ratio of the **width** of kennel A to kennel B.

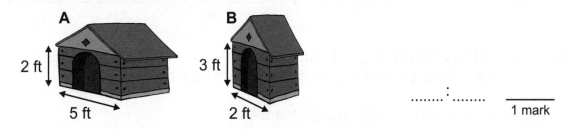

    .... : ....   _____
                                1 mark

    Tom's sausage dog grows by 30 mm every 2 weeks. He says,

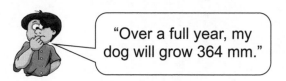

    "Over a full year, my
    dog will grow 364 mm."

    Use estimation to show that Tom is **not** correct.

    ....

    ....

    ....   _____
                                                                                                        2 marks

                        END OF TEST   ┌─────────────┐
                                                             │   │
                                                             │   / 10   │
                                                             └─────────────┘

Warm up

1. What is:

    a) 15% of 80?   b) 55% of 80?

        ....

        2 marks

2. How many seconds are there in:

    a) 3 minutes?   ....   b) 10 minutes?   ....

        1 mark

3. Will and Izzy are meeting in town.
    Will lives 15 miles from town. Izzy lives 26 km from town.

    Who travels the furthest? Tick your answer.
    Use 5 miles = 8 kilometres.

    You must show all of your working.

                                        Will ☐   Izzy ☐   _1 mark_

    It takes Will 1200 seconds to travel into town.

    How many **minutes** does it take Will to travel into town?

                                        .... minutes   _1 mark_

4. Pentagon A is enlarged by a scale factor of 4 to give pentagon B.

7 cm

?? cm

A

B

Diagram not to scale

What is the missing length on pentagon B?

.... cm

1 mark

5. Brooke is making a smoothie. It is made using 60 ml of honey.
The honey makes up 15% of the smoothie.

What is the total volume of the smoothie?

.... ml

2 marks

6. Chloe is organising a pizza party. She orders 9 pizzas and
cuts each one into 8 slices. Each of the 6 adults eats 5 slices
and each child eats 3 slices. There are no slices left over.

How many children are there at the party?

.... children

2 marks

END OF TEST

/ 10

Test 6

Warm up

1. Fill in the gaps to complete these statements.

   a) 21 is [   ] % of 84   b) 8 is [   ] % of 20

   _____
   2 marks

2. Complete this sentence by crossing out the wrong word.

   *A quarter of 160 is (**smaller** / **larger**) than a fifth of 150.*

   _____
   1 mark

3. Ashna is running up a hill.
   For every 10 m she runs, she gains 3 m in elevation.

   How far will Ashna need to run to climb 120 m?

   .... m   _____
                        1 mark

4. There was 40% more rainfall in September than in August.
   There was 15 mm of rainfall in August.

   What was the amount of rainfall in September?

   .... mm   _____
                         1 mark

   The amount of rainfall in August was 20% of
   the amount of rainfall in November.

   What was the amount of rainfall in November?

   .... mm   _____
                         1 mark

5. Abdullah scored 45 marks out of 50 on a maths test.

What percentage did Abdullah score?

.... %

On the maths test, Maggie scored 60%.
On a science test, Maggie scored 120 marks out of 160.

On which test did she score the highest percentage?

You must show all of your working.

Maths ☐   Science ☐

6. Simone is decorating her bathroom using tiles.
She chooses a pattern that uses 5 grey tiles for every 4 white tiles.

In total, she uses 80 white tiles.

How many grey tiles does she use?

.... grey tiles

END OF TEST

/ 10

Warm up

1. What is:

    a) $\frac{4}{7}$ of 14? ....

    b) $\frac{5}{9}$ of 45? ....

    _____
    1 mark

2. Write one of the symbols =, < or > in each
    box to make the statements correct.

    a twelfth of 240 ☐ a fifth of 90

    a seventh of 77 ☐ a sixth of 60

    _____
    2 marks

3. A bakery sells 5 wholemeal loaves for every 2 white loaves
    that they sell. On Tuesday, they sold 63 loaves in total.

    How many wholemeal loaves did they sell on Tuesday?

    .... wholemeal loaves
    _____
    1 mark

4. Patrick makes all the sides of a square 6 times longer.
    He ends up with the square on the right.

    What was the perimeter of the original square?

    36 m

    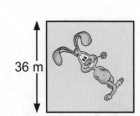

    .... m
    _____
    2 marks

5. Everyone that visited a petting zoo last Saturday was asked to pick their favourite animal. Their answers are shown in the pie chart.

68 people picked a lamb.

How many people picked a llama?

.... people   _____
                         1 mark

How many people visited the petting zoo last Saturday?

.... people   _____
                         1 mark

6. A cargo ship is carrying 840 containers.
This is 42% of the maximum number that it can carry.

What is the maximum number of containers that the cargo ship can carry?

.... containers   _____
                                   2 marks

END OF TEST

/ 10

Test 8

Warm up

1. Given that there are approximately 3 feet in 1 metre, what is:

    a) 15 feet in m? .... m   b) 3 m in feet? .... feet

    _____
    1 mark

2. What is:

    a) 11% of 200?   b) 9% of 4500?

    ....   _____
    2 marks

3. Kobe was 1.3 m tall at the beginning of the year. He measured himself at the end of the year and he was 10% taller.

    How tall was Kobe at the end of the year?

    .... m   _____
    1 mark

4. A theatre has 1 VIP seat for every 8 standard seats. There are 720 standard seats in the theatre.

    How many seats are there in the theatre in total?

    .... seats   _____
    1 mark

16

5. Martin buys a new jumper in the end of season sale.
The price of the jumper is reduced from £50 to £48.

What percentage is the price of the jumper reduced by?

.... %

6. A scale drawing of Mia's garden and garage is shown below.

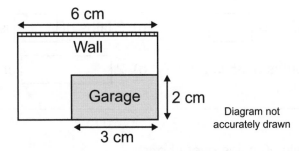

6 cm

Wall

Garage 2 cm

Diagram not
accurately drawn

3 cm

1 cm on the diagram represents 4 m in real life.

What is the length of the wall in real life?

.... m

1 mark

What is the area of Mia's garage in real life?

.... m²

2 marks

END OF TEST

/ 10

Warm up

1. Write the correct number in each of these boxes.

   a) 84 is ☐ times larger than 12.

   b) 96 is ☐ times larger than 8.

   _____
   1 mark

2. Fill in the boxes to complete these sentences.

   a) 3 tenths of 60 is ☐.   b) 2 fifths of ☐ is 8.

   c) ☐ sevenths of 35 is 20.   d) 2 ☐ of 80 is 20.

   _____
   2 marks

3. A coach travels 50 miles every hour.

   How far will it have travelled after 8 hours?

   .... miles   _____
   1 mark

4. Look at the shapes on the right.

   The smaller shape has been
   enlarged to give the larger shape.

   8 mm

   12 mm

   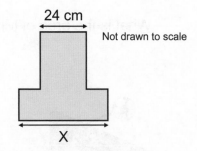

   24 cm

   Not drawn to scale

   X

   What is the length of the side labelled X?

   .... cm   _____
   1 mark

5. The table below shows the distance between Cardiff and four cities.

City	Distance (miles)
Taunton	30
Bridgend	15
Glasgow	300
Chester	120

How many times further away is Cardiff from Chester than from Taunton?

....
1 mark

Glasgow is directly north of Cardiff. Taunton is directly south of Cardiff.

How many times greater is the distance between Glasgow and Taunton than the distance between Bridgend and Cardiff?

....
2 marks

6. Jeff uses 3 slices of ham and 2 slices of bread per sandwich.
A pack of ham contains 63 slices.
A loaf of bread is made up of 14 slices.

How many loaves will Jeff need to use up all of the ham in one pack?

.... loaves
2 marks

END OF TEST

/ 10

Warm up

1. What is:

   a) Two thirds of 18? .... b) A ninth of 81? ....

   c) Three sixths of 54? .... d) Four fifteenths of 45? ....

   2 marks

2. Find the perimeter of the following regular shapes.

   a)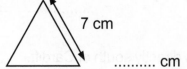

   .... cm

   b)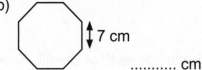

   .... cm

   1 mark

3. Look at these two triangles.

   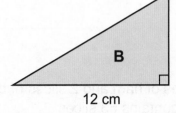

   Not drawn to scale

   Triangle A is enlarged to give triangle B.

   What is the perimeter of triangle B?

   .... cm

   2 marks

4. Val is making a scale model of the Saturn V rocket.
    Her model of the rocket is 22 times smaller.

    The Saturn V rocket was 110 m tall.

    How tall is Val's model?

    110 m

    .... m $\dfrac{}{\text{1 mark}}$

5. Kayla is sailing from Heysham to Douglas.
    She is 9 miles away from Douglas. She is six times
    further away from Heysham than she is from Douglas.

    What is the total distance that Kayla is sailing?

    .... miles $\dfrac{}{\text{2 marks}}$

6. Bembe is making a chocolate and peanut butter milkshake.
    He uses $4\frac{1}{2}$ scoops of chocolate powder for every
    90 g of peanut butter. He uses a total of 15 scoops.

    How much peanut butter does he use?

    .... g $\dfrac{}{\text{2 marks}}$

    END OF TEST   / 10

🕙 **10**

1. Fill in these boxes.

   a) 10% of 300 = ☐   b) 80% of 300 = ☐

   c) 1% of 300 = ☐   d) 87% of 300 = ☐

   _____
   1 mark

2. Fill in these boxes.

   a) 10% of 550 = ☐   b) 30% of 550 = ☐

   c) 2% of 550 = ☐   d) 34% of 300 = ☐

   _____
   1 mark

3. Work out:

   58% of 600   41% of 1800

   ....
                          _____
                          2 marks

4. Dina runs at a steady pace.
   She runs 1500 m in 6 minutes.

   How far can she run in half an hour?

   .... m
   _____
   2 marks

5. Two boxes of cereal are available at the local shop.
    A small box is shown below.

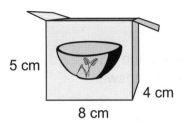

5 cm

4 cm

8 cm

A large box has edges that are twice as long as the small box.

What is the volume of the larger cereal box?

.... cm³   _____
                            2 marks

6. There are 8 penguins for every 3 seals on a beach.
    There is a total of 154 seals and penguins on the beach.

How many more penguins than seals are there on the beach?

.... penguins   _____
                                     2 marks

END OF TEST

/ 10

23   Test 11

(10)

Warm up

1. Some of these shapes are shaded and unshaded in the ratio 3 : 5.
    Which ones? Tick all of the correct answers.

    ☐   ☐   ☐   ☐

    _____
    2 marks

2. 5 miles is approximately 8 km. Approximately, what is:

    a) 50 miles in km?   .... km   b) 40 km in miles?   .... miles

    _____
    1 mark

3. Emma's sunflower grows an average of 6 cm every 7 days.

    How long will it take her sunflower to grow to 126 cm?

    .... days

    _____
    1 mark

4. A group of 50 students are split into two groups.
    The ratio of the number of students in group A to group B is 2 : 3.

    How many students are there in each group?

    Group A: .... students

    Group B: .... students

    _____
    2 marks

5. A farmer is weighing his animals. He notices that
32 sheep weigh the same as 3 cows.

One sheep weighs 75 kg.

Find the weight of one of the farmer's cows.

.... kg

6. The radius of Jupiter is 45 000 miles.
The radius of a passing asteroid is 800 km.

45 000 miles

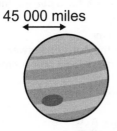

800 km

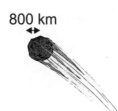

How many times larger is the radius of
Jupiter than the radius of the asteroid?
Use 5 miles = 8 km.

....

END OF TEST

/ 10

Answers

Test 1 – pages 2-3

1. a) 3
   b) 4
   c) 10
   d) 5
   (**2 marks for all four correct,
   otherwise 1 mark for at least two correct**)
2. a) 3 (**1 mark**)
   b) 15 (**1 mark**)
3.

   (**2 marks for all three correct,
   otherwise 1 mark for two correct**)
4. 70 ÷ 35 = 2, so
   7000 ÷ 350 = 20 (**1 mark**)
5. 10% of 240 = 240 ÷ 10 = 24
   240 – 24 = 216 cm (**1 mark**)
6. 6 ÷ 2 = 3, so to convert from 6 people
   to 2 people you divide by 3:
   24 ÷ 3 = 8 cherry tomatoes (**1 mark**)
   390 ÷ 3 = 130 g (**1 mark**)

Test 2 – pages 4-5

1. a) 10
   b) 7
   c) 3
   d) 10
   (**2 marks for all four correct,
   otherwise 1 mark for at least two correct**)
2. a) 6 (**1 mark**)
   b) 4 (**1 mark**)
3. 60 ÷ 15 = 4 m (**1 mark**)
4. 10% of 600 = 600 ÷ 10 = 60
   30% = 10% × 3 = 60 × 3 = £180 (**1 mark**)
5. Box A: £10 ÷ 5 = £2 per card
   Box B: £18 ÷ 10 = £1.80 per card
   So Box B is better value (you save 20p per card)
   (**2 marks for the correct answer,
   otherwise 1 mark for correct working**)

6. E.g. 115 × 2 = 230 cm
   80 × 2 = 160 cm
   230 – 160 = 70 cm
   (**2 marks for the correct answer,
   otherwise 1 mark for a correct method**)

Test 3 – pages 6-7

1. a) 3 (**1 mark**)
   b) 3 (**1 mark**)
   c) 16 (**1 mark**)
   d) 12 (**1 mark**)
2. 35 ÷ 5 = 7
   7 × 2 = 14 minutes (**1 mark**)
3. 18 = 9 × 2
   So width of model is 3 × 2 = 6 cm (**1 mark**)
4. £0.20 × 6 = £1.20
   £1.20 – £1.15 = £0.05
   (**2 marks for the correct answer,
   otherwise 1 mark for a correct method**)
5. 450 ÷ 150 = 3
   750 ÷ 3 = 250 ml
   (**2 marks for the correct answer,
   otherwise 1 mark for a correct method**)

Test 4 – pages 8-9

1. a) 7
   b) 3
   (**1 mark for both correct answers**)
2. a) 1000
   b) 1000
   c) 5000
   d) 80
   (**2 marks for all four correct,
   otherwise 1 mark for at least two correct**)
3. 45 ÷ 3 = 15
   15 × 12 = 180 seconds (**1 mark**)
4. 90 – 54 = 36 °C
   36 ÷ 4 = 9 minutes
   (**2 marks for the correct answer,
   otherwise 1 mark for a correct method**)

5. $350 \div 50 = 7$ (**1 mark**)

6. $5:2$ (**1 mark**)

   There are 52 weeks in a year, so a full year of growth is 30×26 (because $52 \div 2 = 26$). 30×26 is approximately $30 \times 25 = 750$ mm. So Tom's dog will grow approximately 750 mm in one year. 750 mm is a long way from 364 mm, so Tom is wrong.
   (**2 marks for a fully correct explantation, otherwise 1 mark for some correct working**)

Test 5 – pages 10-11

1. a) 12 (**1 mark**)

   b) 44 (**1 mark**)

2. a) 180

   b) 600

   (**1 marks for both answers correct**)

3. $15 \div 5 = 3$
   Will travelled $3 \times 8 = 24$ km.
   So Izzy travelled the furthest.
   (**1 mark for correct answer with working**)
   $1200 \div 60 = 20$ minutes (**1 mark**)

4. $7 \times 4 = 28$ cm (**1 mark**)

5. 15% of the smoothie is 60 ml, so
   1% of the smoothie is $60 \div 15 = 4$ ml.
   100% is $100 \times 4 = 400$ ml.
   (**2 marks for the correct answer, otherwise 1 mark for a correct method**)

6. Total number of slices = $9 \times 8 = 72$
   Number of slices for adults = $6 \times 5 = 30$
   Number of slices for children = $72 - 30 = 42$
   Number of children = $42 \div 3 = 14$
   (**2 marks for the correct answer, otherwise 1 mark for a correct method**)

Test 6 – pages 12-13

1. a) 25% (**1 mark**)

   b) 40% (**1 mark**)

2. *A quarter of 160 is* (~~smaller~~ / **larger**) *than a fifth of 150.* (**1 mark**)

3. $120 \div 3 = 40$
   $40 \times 10 = 400$ m (**1 mark**)

4. 10% of 15 mm = $15 \div 10 = 1.5$ mm
   40% = 10% $\times$ 4 = $1.5 \times 4 = 6$ mm
   $15 + 6 = 21$ mm (**1 mark**)
   20% is 15 mm, so
   100% = 20% $\times$ 5 = $15 \times 5 = 75$ mm (**1 mark**)

5. $\frac{45}{50} = \frac{9}{10} = 90\%$ (**1 mark**)
   $\frac{120}{160} = \frac{12}{16} = \frac{3}{4} = 75\%$
   So Maggie scored a higher percentage on the science test.
   (**1 mark for correct answer with working**)

6. $80 \div 4 = 20$
   $20 \times 5 = 100$ grey tiles
   (**2 marks for the correct answer, otherwise 1 mark for a correct method**)

Test 7 – pages 14-15

1. a) 8

   b) 25

   (**1 mark for both answers correct**)

2. a) a twelfth of 240 > a fifth of 90 (**1 mark**)

   b) a seventh of 77 > a sixth of 60 (**1 mark**)

3. $5 + 2 = 7$ parts
   $63 \div 7 = 9$, so 1 part = 9 loaves
   $9 \times 5 = 45$ loaves (**1 mark**)

4. Side length of original square = $36 \div 6 = 6$ m
   Perimeter = $6 \times 4 = 24$ m
   (**2 marks for the correct answer, otherwise 1 mark for a correct method**)

5. The lamb sector is 90° and the llama sector is 45° — half of 90°.
   So $68 \div 2 = 34$ people picked a llama. (**1 mark**)
   The lamb sector is a quarter of the chart.
   $68 \times 4 = 272$ people (**1 mark**)

6. 1% is $840 \div 42 = 20$ containers.
   100% is $20 \times 100 = 2000$ containers.
   (**2 marks for the correct answer, otherwise 1 mark for a correct method**)

Test 8 – pages 16-17

1. a)   5 m
    b)   9 feet
    (**1 mark for both answers correct**)

2. a)   22 (**1 mark**)
    b)   405 (**1 mark**)

3.   10% of 1.3 m = 1.3 ÷ 10 = 0.13
     1.3 + 0.13 = 1.43 m (**1 mark**)

4.   720 ÷ 8 = 90 VIP seats
     720 + 90 = 810 seats (**1 mark**)

5.   E.g. Reduction = 50 − 48 = £2
     1% of £50 is £0.50, and
     £2 = £0.50 × 4 so £2 = 4% of £50
     So the jumper was reduced by 4%.
     (**2 marks for the correct answer,
     otherwise 1 mark for a correct method**)

6.   5 × 4 = 20 m (**1 mark**)
     3 × 4 = 12 m
     2 × 4 = 8 m
     So the area = 12 × 8 = 96 m².
     (**2 marks for the correct answer,
     otherwise 1 mark for a correct method**)

Test 9 – pages 18-19

1. a)   7
    b)   12
    (**1 mark for both answers correct**)

2. a)   18
    b)   20
    c)   4
    d)   eighths
    (**2 marks for all four correct answers,
    otherwise 1 mark for at least two correct**)

3.   50 × 8 = 400 miles (**1 mark**)

4.   24 = 8 × 3
     X = 12 × 3 = 36 cm (**1 mark**)

5.   120 ÷ 30 = 4 (**1 mark**)
     300 + 30 = 330
     330 ÷ 15 = 22
     (**2 marks for the correct answer,
     otherwise 1 mark for a correct method**)

6.   Number of sandwiches = 63 ÷ 3 = 21
     Number of slices of bread = 21 × 2 = 42
     Number of loaves = 42 ÷ 14 = 3
     (**2 marks for the correct answer,
     otherwise 1 mark for a correct method**)

Test 10 – pages 20-21

1. a)   12
    b)   9
    c)   27
    d)   12
    (**2 marks for all four correct answers,
    otherwise 1 mark for at least two correct**)

2. a)   21 cm
    b)   56 cm
    (**1 mark for both answers correct**)

3.   The sides of triangle B are 12 ÷ 4 = 3 times
     longer than the sides of triangle A.
     The missing sides are 3 × 3 = 9 cm
     and 5 × 3 = 15 cm.
     Perimeter = 12 + 9 + 15 = 36 cm
     (**2 marks for the correct answer,
     otherwise 1 mark for a correct method**)

4.   110 ÷ 22 = 5 m (**1 mark**)

5.   Kayla is 9 × 6 = 54 miles away from Heysham.
     So the distance she is sailing is
     54 + 9 = 63 miles.
     (**2 marks for the correct answer,
     otherwise 1 mark for a correct method**)

6.   There are 4.5 scoops for every 90 g
     of peanut butter, so there is 1 scoop
     per 90 ÷ 4.5 = 20 g of peanut butter.
     15 scoops means 15 × 20 = 300 g
     of peanut butter.
     (**2 marks for the correct answer,
     otherwise 1 mark for a correct method**)

Test 11 – pages 22-23

1. a) 30
    b) 240
    c) 3
    d) 261
    (**1 mark for all four correct answers**)

2. a) 55
    b) 165
    c) 11
    d) 187
    (**1 mark for all four correct answers**)

3. 50% of 600 = 600 ÷ 2 = 300
    1% of 600 = 600 ÷ 100 = 6
    8% of 600 = 8 × 6 = 48
    58% of 600 = 300 + 48 = 348 (**1 mark**)

    10% of 1800 = 1800 ÷ 10 = 180
    40% of 1800 = 4 × 180 = 720
    1% of 1800 = 180 ÷ 10 = 18
    41% of 1800 = 720 + 18 = 738 (**1 mark**)

4. Half an hour is 30 minutes.
    30 ÷ 6 = 5
    5 × 1500 = 7500 m
    (**2 marks for the correct answer,
    otherwise 1 mark for a correct method**)

5. 5 × 2 = 10   8 × 2 = 16   4 × 2 = 8
    16 × 8 = 128
    128 × 10 = 1280 cm^3
    (**2 marks for the correct answer,
    otherwise 1 mark for a correct method**)

6. E.g. 8 + 3 = 11 and 154 ÷ 11 = 14
    Difference = 8 – 3 = 5 and 14 × 5 = 70
    So there are 70 more penguins.
    (**2 marks for the correct answer,
    otherwise 1 mark for a correct method**)

Test 12 – pages 24-25

1.
    (**1 mark for each correct answer**)

2. a) 80 km
    b) 25 miles
    (**1 mark for both answers correct**)

3. 126 ÷ 6 = 21
    21 × 7 = 147 days (**1 mark**)

4. 2 + 3 = 5 and 50 ÷ 5 = 10
    Group A = 10 × 2 = 20 students
    Group B = 10 × 3 = 30 students
    (**2 marks for the correct answer,
    otherwise 1 mark for a correct method**)

5. 32 sheep weigh:

    ```
          7 5
        ×  3 2
        1 5,0
      + 2 2,5 0
        2 4 0 0  kg
            ₁
    ```

    2400 ÷ 3 = 800 kg
    (**2 marks for the correct answer,
    otherwise 1 mark for a correct method**)

6. E.g. 800 ÷ 8 = 100
    100 × 5 = 500 miles
    45 000 ÷ 500 = 90
    (**2 marks for the correct answer,
    otherwise 1 mark for a correct method**)

Answers

Progress Chart

That's all the tests in the book done — nice one!

Now fill in this table with all of your scores and see how you got on.

	Score
Test 1	
Test 2	
Test 3	
Test 4	
Test 5	
Test 6	
Test 7	
Test 8	
Test 9	
Test 10	
Test 11	
Test 12	

30

CGP books – the ultimate Key Stage Two survival kit!

Grammar, geometry, the ancient Greeks... millions of pupils aged 7 to 11 use CGP books to conquer the challenges of KS2! It's easy to order from us (with next-day delivery), online or by phone:

www.cgpbooks.co.uk • 0800 1712 712

Or you'll find our range in any good bookshop, including:

 Waterstones

CGP

Scale up your KS2 Ratio and Proportion prep!

CGP's terrific 10-Minute Tests are a great way to prepare for the SATS...

- **Short and snappy KS2 Maths tests...**
  You bet — ideal for speedy practice sessions

- **Plenty of Ratio and Proportion questions...**
  Yep, they'll really test how much you know

- **Full answers and a progress chart...**
  So checking your work couldn't be easier!

P.S.   Looking for more practice? We have two books of 10-Minute Tests covering **every Maths topic**!

To avoid dropping off the edge, keep to the middle

ISBN 978 1 78908 453 5

9 781789 084535

CGP

MRPXP21   £2.95
                (Retail Price)

www.cgpbooks.co.uk